KINDERGARTEN

Treasures

Practice Book

Macmillan/McGraw-Hill

Contents

Name _ojfbick_

The Alphabet

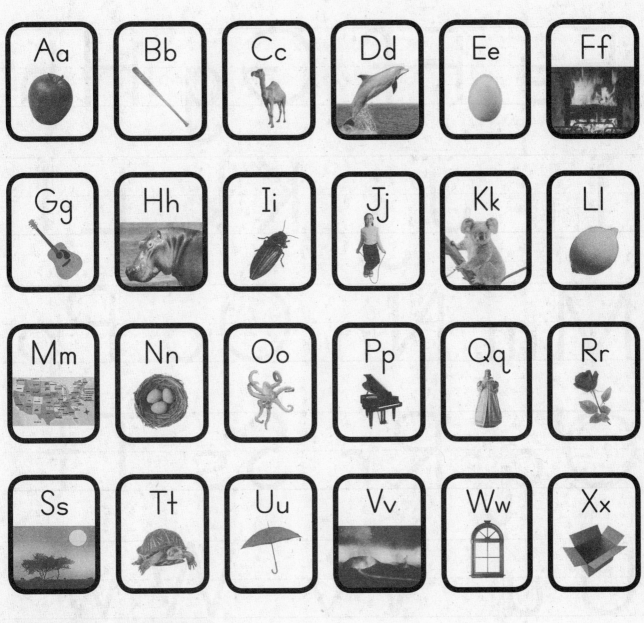

Draw

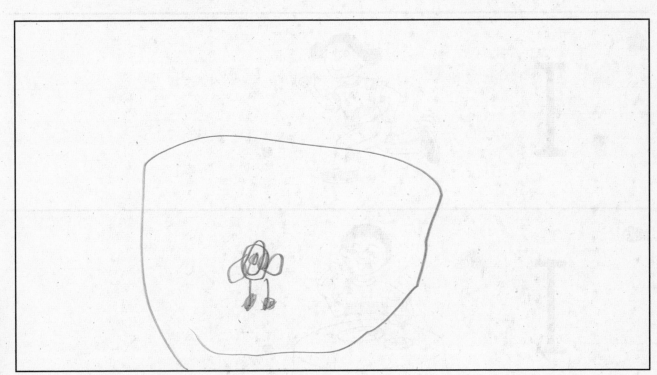

©Macmillan/McGraw-Hill

Respond to the Big Book: *Animals in the Park: An ABC Book*
Name the animals. Then draw another animal from the story.

Name _____

I

I

I

I

High-Frequency Word: *I*
Read the sentences: *I draw. I read. I run. I eat.*

Aa Bb Cc Dd Ee Ff Gg Hh Ii Jj Kk Ll Mm
Nn Oo Pp Qq Rr Ss Tt Uu Vv Ww Xx Yy Zz

Letter Recognition: *Aa - Dd*
Name each letter. Draw a line to connect the capital and
lowercase forms of the same letter.

Name _____

Aa Bb Cc Dd Ee Ff Gg Hh Ii Jj Kk Ll Mm
Nn Oo Pp Qq Rr Ss Tt Uu Vv Ww Xx Yy Zz

Letter Recognition: *Ee - Hh*
Name each letter. Draw a line to connect the capital and
lowercase forms of the same letter.

Name _____

I

3

I
sleep

I

3

I
run

©Macmillan/McGraw-Hill

High-Frequency Word: *I*
Read the book aloud to a partner.

4   Start Smart: We Are Special • Week I

1

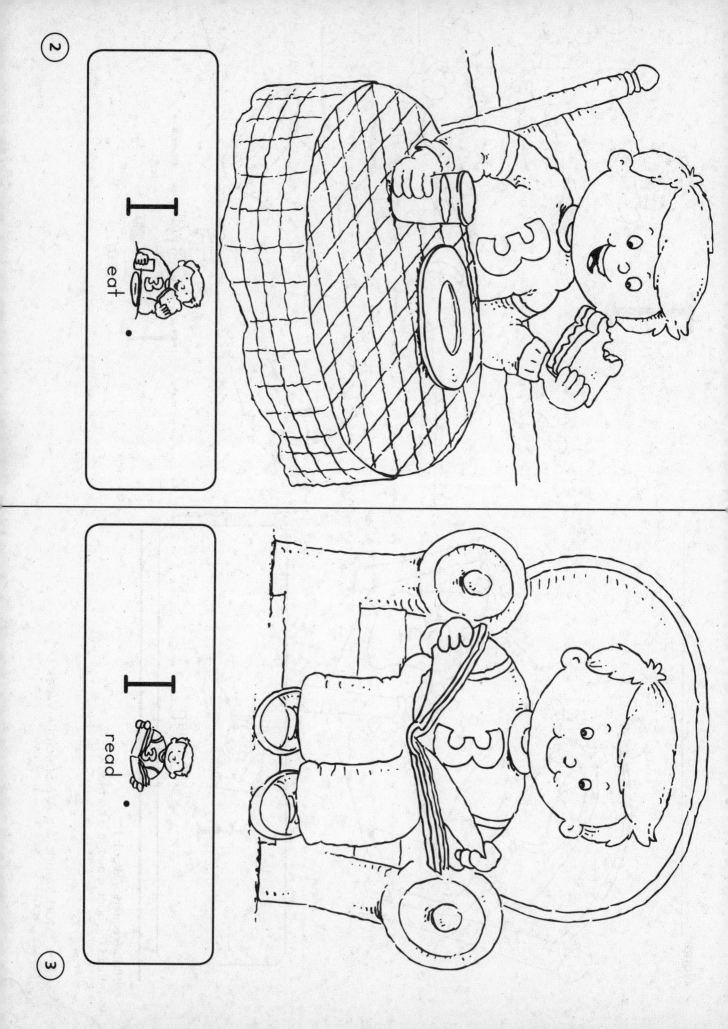

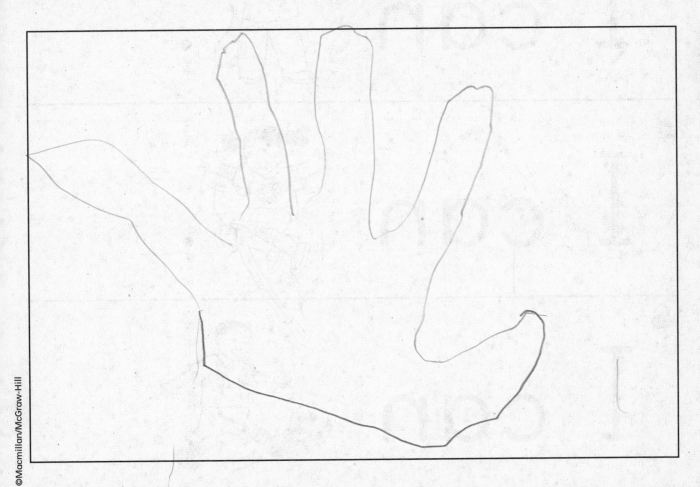

Respond to the Big Book: *Hands Can*
Talk about what the children are doing in the pictures.
Trace your hand and tell a partner what your hands can do.

Name _____

I can ____ .

I can ____ .

I can ____ .

I can ____ .

High-Frequency Word: *can*
Read the sentences: *I can clap. I can sing. I can jump. I can kick.*

Aa Bb Cc Dd Ee Ff Gg Hh Ii Jj Kk Ll Mm
Nn Oo Pp Qq Rr Ss Tt Uu Vv Ww Xx Yy Zz

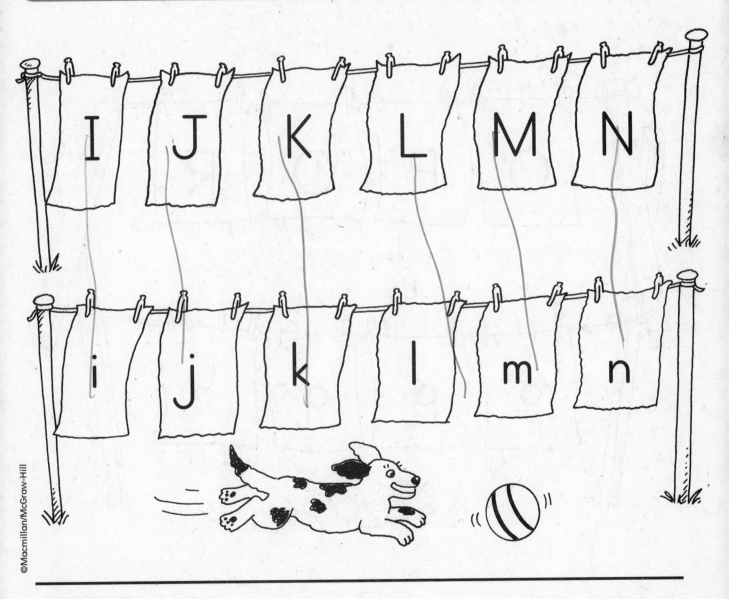

Letter Recognition: *Ii - Nn*
Name each letter. Draw a line to connect the capital and
lowercase forms of the same letter.

Name _____

Aa Bb Cc Dd Ee Ff Gg Hh Ii Jj Kk Ll Mm
Nn Oo Pp Qq Rr Ss Tt Uu Vv Ww Xx Yy Zz

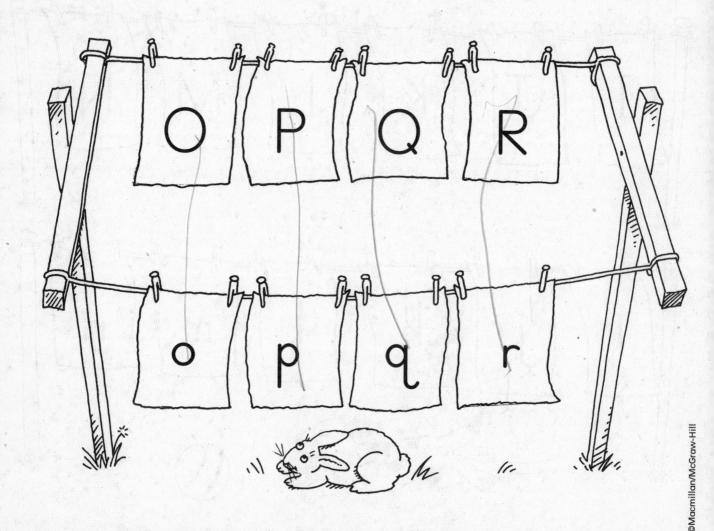

Letter Recognition: Oo - Rr
Name each letter. Draw a line to connect the capital and
lowercase forms of the same letter.

©Macmillan/McGraw-Hill

I Can

I can
wash.

Name _____

I can
sleep.

High-Frequency Word: can
Read the book aloud to a partner.

4   Start Smart: We Are Special • Week 2

I can

brush.

I can

hug.

Respond to the Big Book: *Jazz Baby*
Look at the pictures and name the instruments. Draw a circle
around the two pictures that are the same. Which picture
is different?

Name _____

I can  .

I can  .

I can  .

I can  .

High-Frequency Words: *I, can*
Read the sentences: *I can sing. I can dance. I can play. I can clap.*

Aa Bb Cc Dd Ee Ff Gg Hh Ii Jj Kk Ll Mm
Nn Oo Pp Qq Rr Ss Tt Uu Vv Ww Xx Yy Zz

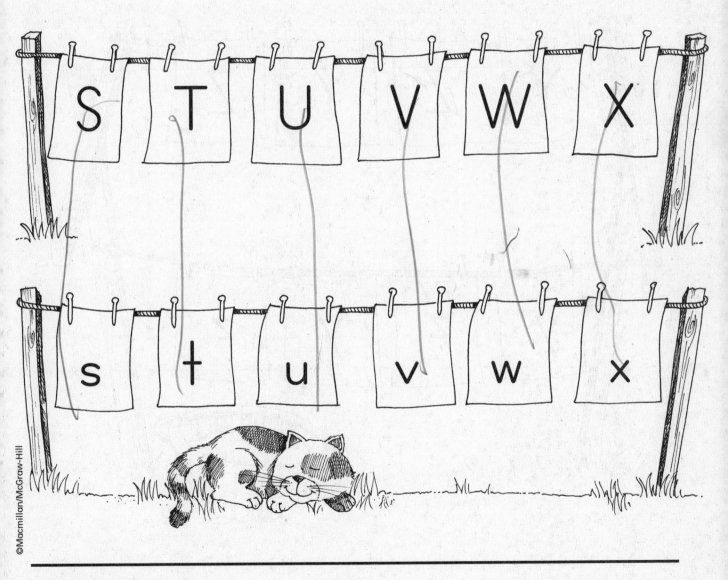

Letter Recognition: *Ss - Xx*
Name each letter. Draw a line to connect the capital and
lowercase forms of the same letter.

Aa Bb Cc Dd Ee Ff Gg Hh Ii Jj Kk Ll Mm
Nn Oo Pp Qq Rr Ss Tt Uu Vv Ww Xx Yy Zz

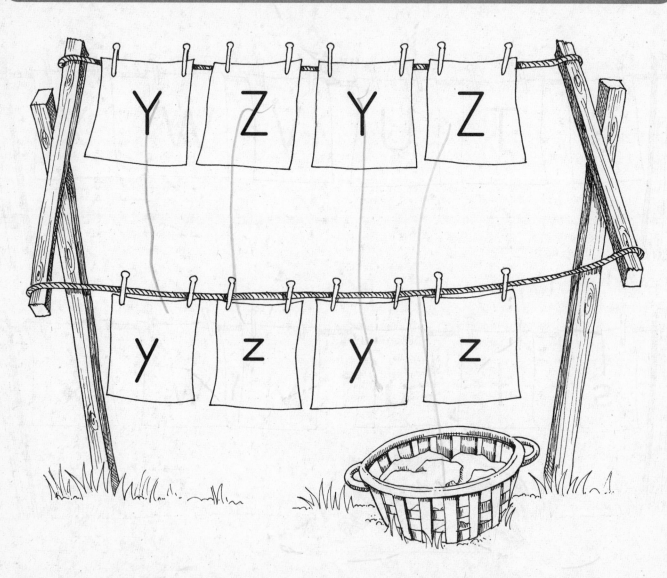

Letter Recognition: *Yy - Zz*
Name each letter. Draw a line to connect the capital and
lowercase forms of the same letter.

I Can

I can
run

I can
clap

Name _____

©Macmillan/McGraw-Hill

High-Frequency Words: *I, can*
Read the book aloud to a partner.

4   Start Smart: We Are Special • Week 3

I can

kick

I can

jump

Mm

Name _____

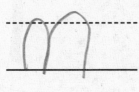  

Phonics: /m/*m*
Look at the picture. Say the name of each item. Circle each
item whose name begins with the same sound as *monkey*.
Write the letter.

Unit I: Families • Week I   **21**

Name _____

Comprehension: Make Predictions *Whose Baby Am I?*
Look at the baby animals. Name each animal.
Draw a line from the baby animal to the adult animal you
think it will grow into.

We Can

We can
paint.

①

Name

ABCDEFGHIJKLM
NOPQRSTUVWXYZ
abcdefghijk
lmnopqrst
uvwxyz

We can
hug.

High-Frequency Word: we
Read the book aloud to a
partner. Reread for fluency.

④ Unit 1: Families • Week 1

We can write.

We can read.

2

3

Phonemic Awareness: /m/

Look at the pictures. Say the name of each item. Circle the item if
its name begins with the same sound you hear at the beginning
of *monkey*.

Name _____

 Mm

   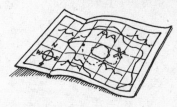

_____ _____ _____

m

  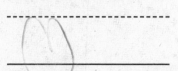 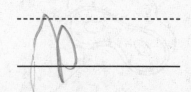

_____ _____ _____

   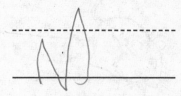

_____ _____ _____

   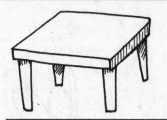

_____ _____ _____

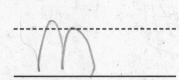 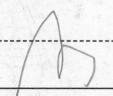 

Phonics: /m/m
Say the name of each picture. Write the letter below
each picture whose name begins with the /m/ sound.

Aa

_a_

Phonics: /a/a
Look at the picture. Say the name of each item. Circle each item
whose name begins with the same sound as *apple*. Write the letter.

Comprehension: Setting

🍎 Circle the picture that shows a family working in a garden.

⭐ Circle the picture that shows a family at the store.

©Macmillan/McGraw-Hill

The

the

boy

Name

the

dog

High-Frequency Word: *the*
Read the book aloud to a partner.
Reread for fluency.

4 Unit I: Families • Week 2

1

the

girl

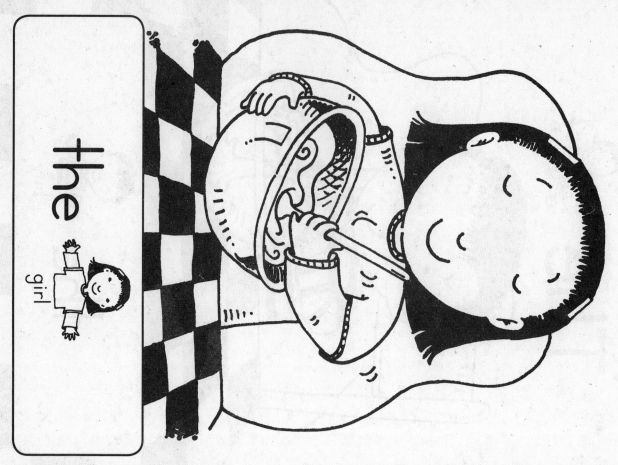

the

mom

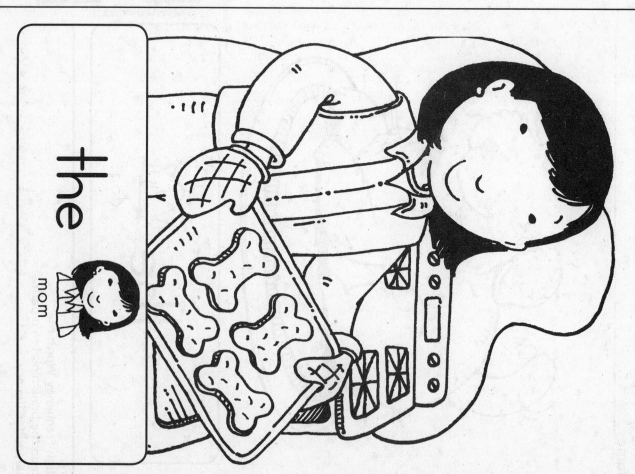

Phonemic Awareness: /a/
Look at the picture. Say the name of each item. Circle the
item if its name begins with the same sound you hear at the
beginning of *astronaut*.

Unit I: Families • Week 2   31

Name _____

I <u>am</u>  .

happy

I _____  .

sad

I _____  .

mad

Phonics: Blending *am*
Blend the sounds and say the word.
Read the sentence. Write the word. Read the sentence again.

©Macmillan/McGraw-Hill

Mm

Name _____

_____   _____   _____

- - - - - - -   m   - - - - - - -

_____   _____   _____

   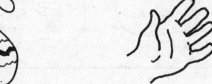   

_____   _____   _____

- - - - - - -   - - - - - - -   - - - - - - -

_____   _____   _____

   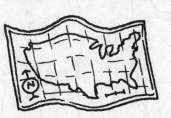   

_____   _____   _____

- - - - - - -   - - - - - - -   - - - - - - -

_____   _____   _____

©Macmillan/McGraw-Hill

Phonics: /m/m
Say the name of each picture. Write the letter below each
picture whose name begins with the /m/ sound.

Unit I: Families • Week 3   **33**

Comprehension: Make Predictions
Look at the big picture. Tell what is happening. Circle the picture
that shows what might happen next.

Name _____

I can

I can _____.
run

We can _____.
eat

©Macmillan/McGraw-Hill

High-Frequency Words: *we, the*
Read the book aloud to a
partner. Reread for fluency.

4   Unit I: Families • Week 3

1

We can run !!! .

The dog can run .

A a

Name _____

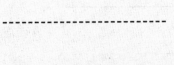

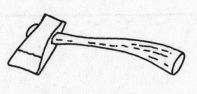

Phonics: /a/a
Say the name of each picture. Write the letter below each
picture whose name begins with the /a/ sound.

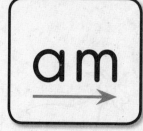

I <u>_____</u>

am .

mad

★

I _____

.

sad

I _____

.

happy

Phonics: Blending *am*
Blend the sounds and say the word. Read the sentence.
Write the word *am*. Read the sentence again.

©Macmillan/McGraw-Hill

Phonics: /m/m and /a/a
Cut out the pictures. Say the name of each picture. Glue it below
the monkey if it begins with the /m/ sound. Glue it below the
alligator if it begins with the /a/ sound.

Name _____

Name

Name

Phonics: /m/m and /a/a
Say the name of each animal and its beginning sound and letter.
Write your name. Cut out the bookmarks. Use them to hold your
place when reading a book.

40 Unit I: Families • Week 3

Name _____

©Macmillan/McGraw-Hill

S

_____

- -

_____

Phonics: /s/s

Look at the picture. Say the name of each item. Circle each item whose name begins with the same sound as *sun*. Write the letter.

Name _____

Comprehension: Character

🍎 Circle the picture that shows two characters working together.

⭐ Circle the picture that shows a character painting.

🌲 Circle the picture that shows two characters reading together.

42 Unit 2: Friends • Week 1

We Like Sam!

We like

apples

①

©Macmillan/McGraw-Hill

Name

We like

Sam

High-Frequency Word: *like*
Read the book aloud to a partner.
Reread for fluency.

④ Unit 2: Friends • Week 1

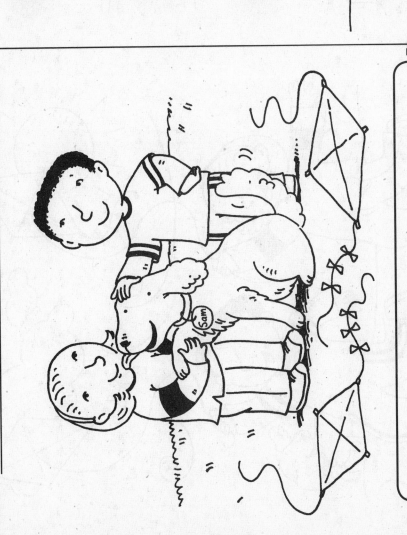

We like

sandwiches

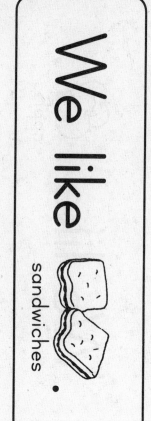

We like

kites

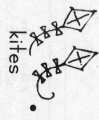

Phonemic Awareness: /s/
Look at the picture. Say the name of each item. Circle the item if its
name begins with the same sound you hear at the beginning of *sun*.

Sam →

Am I Sam ?

★

I am _____ .

I like _____ .

Phonics: Blending s
Blend the sounds and say the word. Read the sentence.
Write the word *Sam*. Read the sentence again.

Pp

Name _____

p

Phonics: /p/p

Look at the picture. Say the name of each item. Circle each item
whose name begins with the same sound as *pig*. Write the letter.

Unit 2: Friends • Week 2   **47**

Comprehension: Compare and Contrast
Look at the picture. Circle all of the food. Draw a line under
the fruit. Talk with a partner about how the fruit is the same
and different from the other foods.

I Like

I like a 🍑 .
peach

I like a 🍒 .
cherry

Name _____

High-Frequency Word: a
Read the book aloud to a partner.
Reread for fluency.

④ Unit 2: Friends • Week 2

I like a .

pear

I like a .

banana

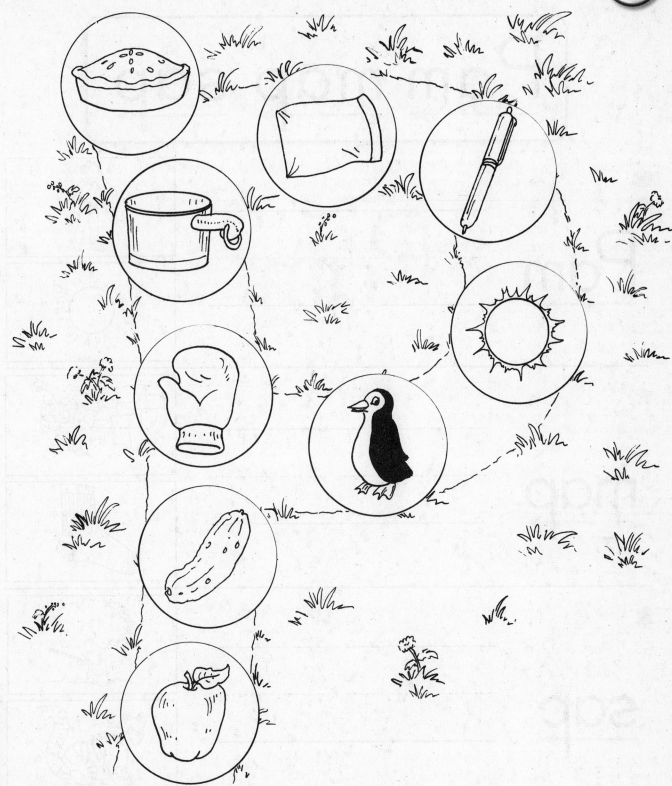

Phonemic Awareness: /p/
Look at the picture. Say the name of each item on the path.
Color the item if its name begins with the same sound you
hear at the beginning of *path*.

Name _____

Pam map sap

Pam _____ Pam

map _____

sap _____

Phonics: Blending with /p/p
Blend the sounds and say the word. Write the word. Then circle the picture that goes with the word.

Ss

Name _____

S

Phonics: /s/s

Look at the picture. Say the name of each item. Circle each item
whose name begins with the same sound as *sun*. Write the letter.

Unit 2: Friends • Week 3   53

Name _____

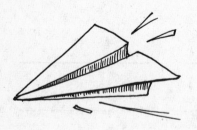

Comprehension: Character *Simon and Molly plus Hester*
Name the characters. Then draw a line to match the
characters to what they do with a friend in the story.

We Like

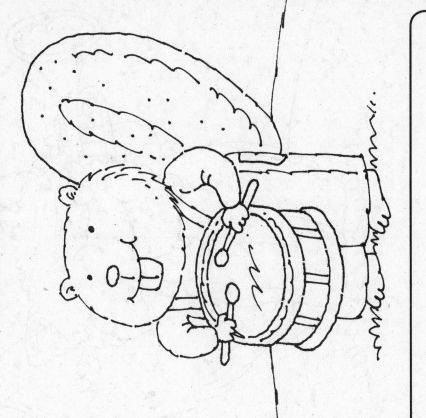

I like a .
drum

Name _____

We like .
music

High-Frequency Words: *like, a*
Read the book aloud to a
partner. Reread for fluency.

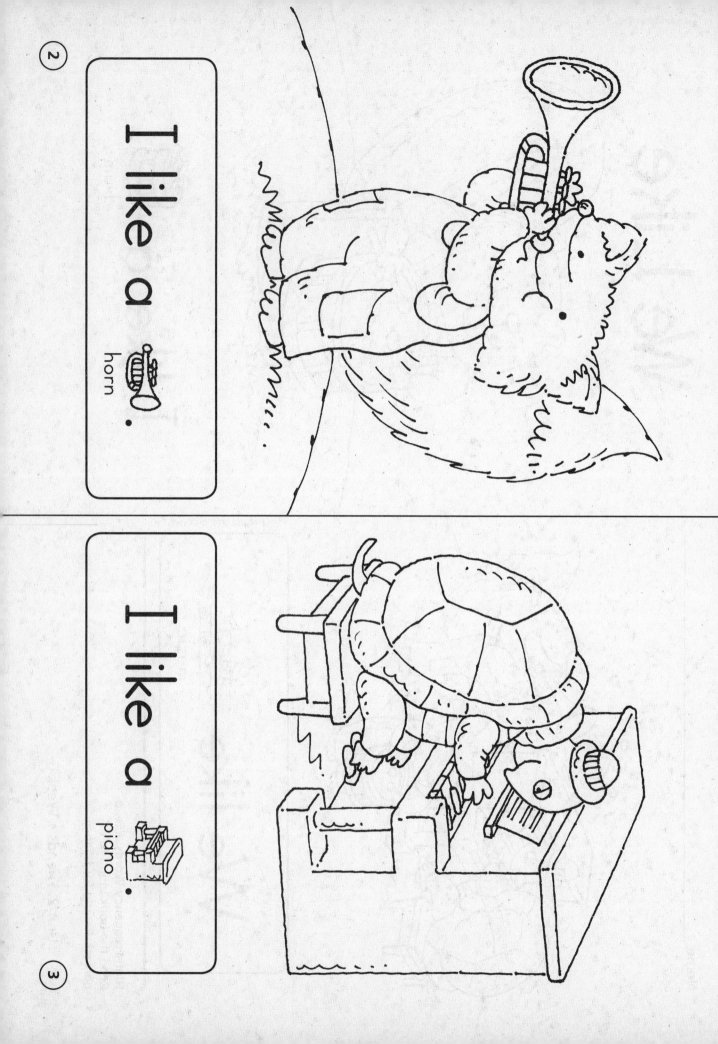

I like a 🎺.
horn

I like a 🪗.
piano

Pp

Name _____

p

Phonics: /p/p
Say the name of each picture. Write the letter below
each picture whose name begins with the /p/ sound.

Unit 2: Friends • Week 3   57

Name _____

Sam Pam map sap

Sam | Sam |

Pam | |

map | |

sap | |

Phonics: Blending s, p
Blend the sounds and say the word. Write the word.
Repeat the word.

Phonemic Awareness: /s/, /p/
Say the name of each picture. Put a marker on each picture if its
name begins with the /p/ sound.
Play again. Put a marker on each picture if its name begins with the
/s/ sound.

Name _____

Phonics: /s/s, /p/p
Say the name of each picture. Write the letter that stands for the
sound you hear at the beginning of each word.

60 Unit 2: Friends • Week 3

©Macmillan/McGraw-Hill

Tt

Write

©Macmillan/McGraw-Hill

t

Phonics: /t/t
Look at the picture. Say the name of each item. Circle each item
whose name begins with the same sound as *turtle*. Write the letter.

Unit 3: Transportation • Week I   61

©Macmillan/McGraw-Hill

Comprehension: Make Predictions

Look at the top picture. Draw a line to the picture below that shows
what might happen next.

I See Pam!

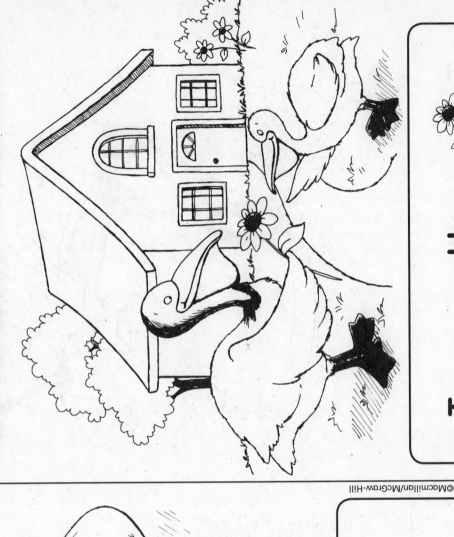

I see the .

I see

flower

①

Name _____

I see Pam!

I see

High-Frequency Word: *see*
Read the book aloud to a partner.
Reread for fluency.

④ Unit 3: Transportation • Week 1

I see the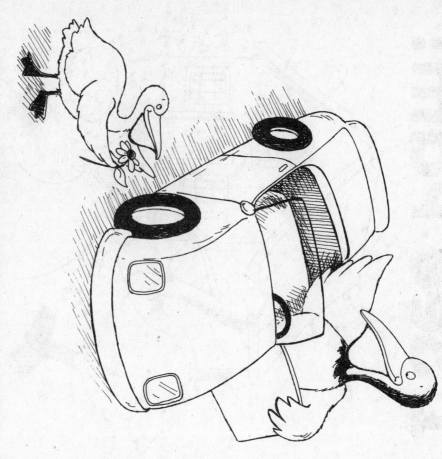

car.

I see the

plane.

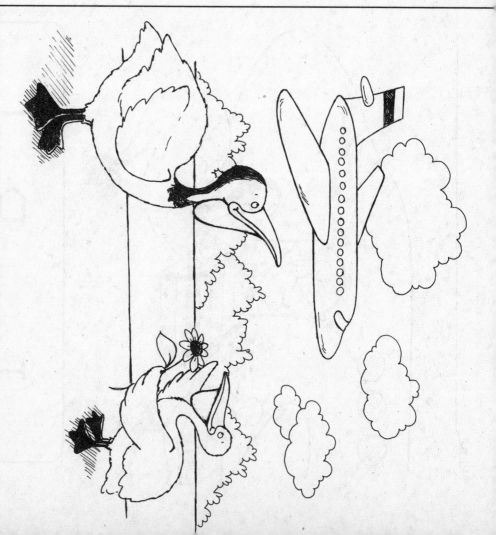

Phonemic Awareness: /t/

Look at the pictures. Say the name of each item. Color the item if its name begins with the same sound you hear at the beginning of *turtle*.

Name _____

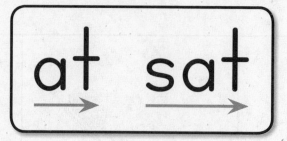

at sat

I am ___at___ the  .
school

I _____ at the  .
table

I am _____ the  .
house

Phonics: Blending _at_
Blend the sounds and say the word. Read the sentence. Write the
word that completes the sentence. Read the sentence again.

I i

Name _____

i

Phonics: /i/i
Look at the picture. Say the name of each item on the path.
Circle each item whose name begins with the same sound as
iguana. Write the letter.

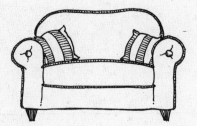  

 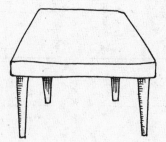 

Vocabulary: Classify and Categorize
Name the pictures in each row. Draw an X on the picture that does
not belong. Tell why it does not belong.

Can We Go?

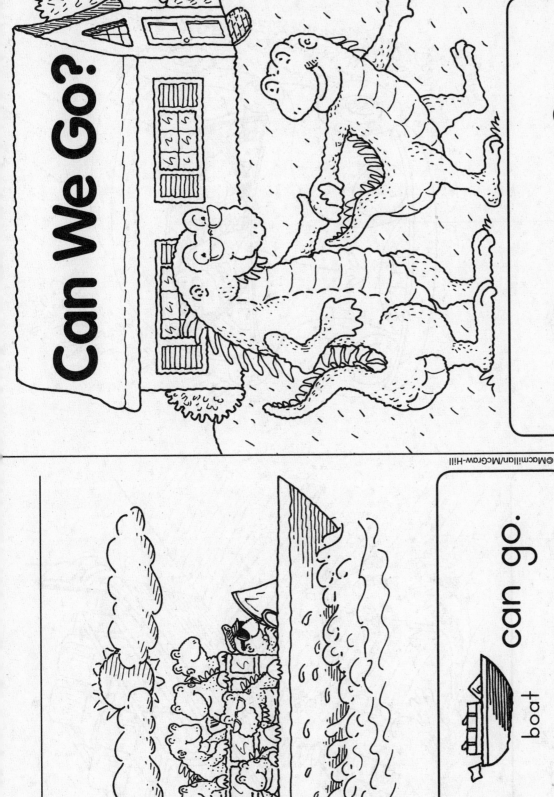

Can we go?

1

Name

The can go.

boat

High-Frequency Word: *go*
Read the book aloud to a partner.
Reread for fluency.

4   Unit 3: Transportation • Week 2

We can go!

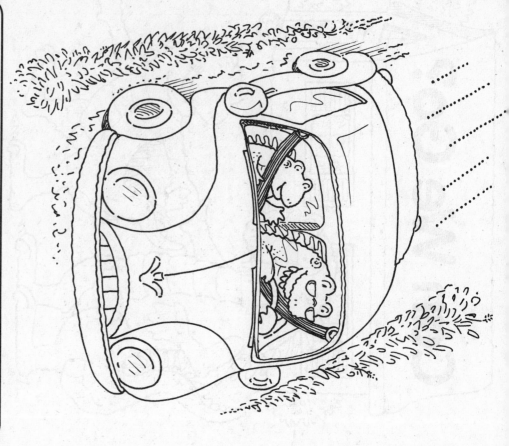

We see the  boat.

Phonemic Awareness: /i/
Look at the pictures. Say the name of each item. Circle the
item if its name begins with the same sound you hear at the
beginning of *inchworm*.

Name _____

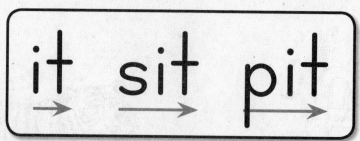

it
→

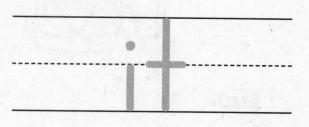

sit
→

_____

pit
→

_____

Phonics: Blending _it_
Blend the sounds and say the word. Write the word. Repeat the word.

Tt

Name _____

t

Phonics: /t/t
Say the name of each picture. Write the letter below each picture
whose name begins with the /t/ sound.

Unit 3: Transportation • Week 3   **73**

Comprehension: Character, Plot *Duck on a Bike*

 Circle the picture that shows what happened at the beginning of the story.

★ Circle the character who always wanted to ride a bike.

We Can Go!

We see a bike.

1

©Macmillan/McGraw-Hill

Name _____

We like the bike.

High-Frequency Words: *see, go*
Read the book aloud to a partner.
Reread for fluency.

4 Unit 3: Transportation • Week 3

Can we go?

We can go!

Ii

Ink

i

Soap

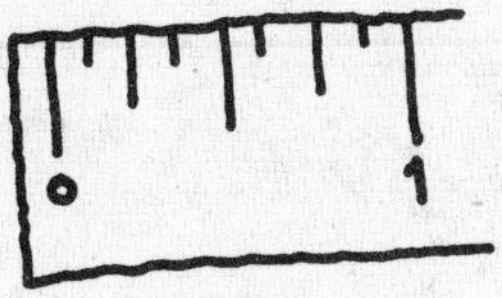

Phonics: /i/i
Say the name of each picture. Write the letter below each picture
whose name begins with the /i/ sound.

it sit Pat

We see 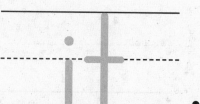 .

It can _____ .

We like _____ .

Phonics: Blending /i/i, /t/t
Blend the sounds and say each word. Read the sentence. Write the
word that completes the sentence. Read the sentence again.

©Macmillan/McGraw-Hill

Draw

Ink

Tt

You're Invited Party

Phonics: /t/*t*
Say the name of each picture. Draw a line from the pictures that
begin with the /t/ sound to the tent.

Name _____

Ii

Ink

Phonics: /i/i
Say the name of each picture. Draw a line from the pictures that
begin with the /i/ sound to the *iguana*.

Nn

n

9

Phonics: /n/*n*
Say the name of each picture. Write the letter next to each picture
whose name begins with the /n/ sound.

Name _____

Comprehension: Sequence *Apple Farmer Annie*
Look at the pictures. Write 1, 2, and 3 to show what happened first, next, and last.

Nip, Nat

Name _____

We like to go.

We like to sit.

©Macmillan/McGraw-Hill

(1)

High-Frequency Word: *to*
Read the book aloud to a partner.
Reread for fluency.

(4) Unit 4: Food • Week 1

We like to  nap.

We like to see.

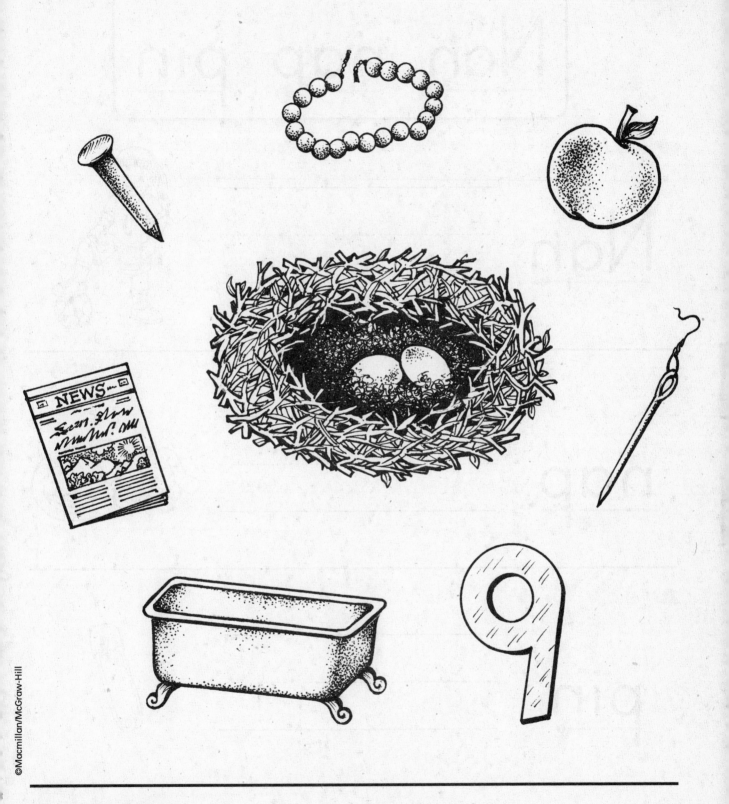

Phonemic Awareness: /n/
Look at the pictures. Say the name of each item. Circle the item if its
name begins with the same sound you hear at the beginning of *nest*.

Nan nap pin

Nan Nan

nap

pin

Phonics: Blending n
Blend the sounds and say the word. Write the word. Repeat the word.

Cc

Name _____

C

©Macmillan/McGraw-Hill

Phonics: /k/c

Say the name of each picture. Write the letter next to each
picture whose name begins with the /k/ sound.

Comprehension: Make Inferences
Look at the pictures. Draw a line from each worker to the place
where he or she works. Talk about what each worker does.

©Macmillan/McGraw-Hill

I Have a

cat

I have a .

cat

I have to go.

I have a .

cat

©Macmillan/McGraw-Hill

High-Frequency Word: *have*
Read the book aloud to a
partner. Reread for fluency.

④ Unit 4: Food • Week 2

①

I have a  .

can

I have a .

cap

Phonemic Awareness: /k/c
Look at the picture. Say the name of each item. Circle the item
if its name begins with the same sound that you hear at the
beginning of *cat*.

Name _____

Cam cap can cat

Cam  Cam

cap

can

cat

©Macmillan/McGraw-Hill

Phonics: Blending c
Blend the sounds and say the word. Write the word. Repeat the word.

n

Phonics: /n/*n*

Say the name of each picture. Write the letter next to each picture
whose name begins with the /n/ sound.

Name _____

🍎

⭐

Comprehension: Make Inferences
Look at the top picture. Then look at the pictures below. Draw a line
to the picture below that shows what the characters might do.

I Nap

I have to nap.

1

Name _____

I have to sip.

I have to

High-Frequency Words: *to, have*
Read the book aloud to a partner.
Reread for fluency.

4 Unit 4: Food • Week 3

I have to pin.

I have to sit.

Cc

Name _____

Write

©Macmillan/McGraw-Hill

C

Phonics: /k/c

Look at the picture. Say the name of each item. Circle each item whose name begins with the same sound as *cat*. Write the letter.

Unit 4: Food • Week 3   **97**

Nan can nap

I am Nan.

I _____ tap.

I can _____ .

Phonics: Blending *n, c*
Blend the sounds and say the word. Read the sentence.
Write the word that completes the sentence. Read the sentence again.

©Macmillan/McGraw-Hill

Name _____

©Macmillan/McGraw-Hill

Phonics: /n/n, /k/c
Say the name of each item and the letter it begins with. Turn the
picture over and trace the letter.

Unit 4: Food • Week 3   99

c   n   c   c

c   n   n   c

n   c   n   n

Phonics: /n/n, /k/c
Trace the letters. Say each letter and its sound.
Name a word that begins with the letter.

Name _____

Phonics: /o/o
Say the name of each picture. Write the letter next to
each picture whose name begins with the /o/ sound.

Unit 5: Animals • Week 1   101

Draw

Name _____

Comprehension: Make Predictions *Mama Cat Has Three Kittens*
Look at the big picture. Then look at the two small pictures. Draw
a line to the picture that shows what might happen next.

It Is!

It is in the  tree.

Name ___

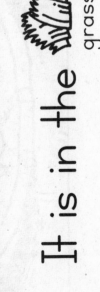

It is in the grass.

High-Frequency Word: *is*
Read the book aloud to a partner.
Reread for fluency.

4 Unit 5: Animals • Week 1

It is in the

flowers .

It is in the

log .

  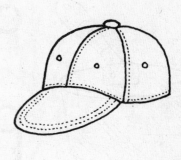

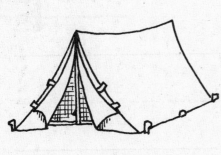  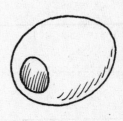

Phonemic Awareness: /o/

Say the name of each picture. Circle the picture if its name begins
with the same sound you hear at the beginning of *octopus*.

cot

pot

pot

pop

pan

_____

mom

mat

_____

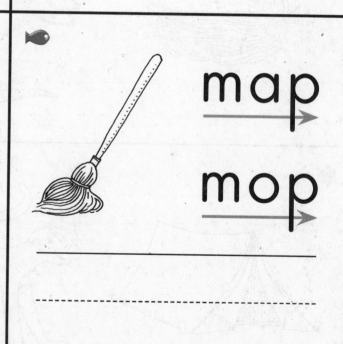

map

mop

_____

©Macmillan/McGraw-Hill

Phonics: Blending /o/o
Blend the sounds and say each word. Then circle the word that
names the picture. Write the word that names the picture.

Ff

Name _____

Phonics: /f/f
Say the name of each picture. Write the letter next to
each picture whose name begins with the /f/ sound.

Name _____

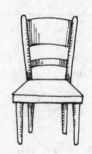

Comprehension: Classify and Categorize

Say the name of each item. Circle the animals. Draw a line under the things that are not animals.

Name _____

Play

A ___ can play.
pig

©Macmillan/McGraw-Hill

High-Frequency Word: play
Read the book aloud to a partner.
Reread for fluency.

A ___ can play.
dog

4 Unit 5: Animals • Week 2

1

A
cub
can play.

A 🐟
fish
can play.

Phonemic Awareness: /f/
Look at the picture. Say the name of each item. Circle the item
if its name begins with the same sound you hear at the beginning
of *fish*.

Name _____

fan fit fin

I have a ___fan___ .

Can it _____ ?

I see a _____ .

Phonics: Blending f
Blend the sounds and say each word. Read the sentence. Write the
word that completes the sentence. Read the sentence again.

©Macmillan/McGraw-Hill

Name _____

©Macmillan/McGraw-Hill

Phonics: /o/o
Say the name of each picture. Circle each picture whose name
begins with the same sound as *octopus*. Write the letter.

Unit 5: Animals • Week 3   **113**

Name _____

Comprehension: Plot, Character *Mole and the Baby Bird*
Draw a line to match the characters to what they did in the story.

Cam

Cam is a cat.

Name _____

Cam can play in a cap.

High-Frequency Words: *is, play*
Read the book aloud to a partner.
Reread for fluency.

④ Unit 5: Animals • Week 3

①

Cam is fat!

Cam can play in a  hat.

hat

Write

Ff Name _____

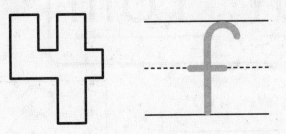

4  — f — 6 _____

 ★ 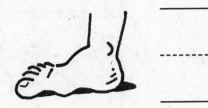 _____  _____

🌲  _____  _____

  _____ _____

©Macmillan/McGraw-Hill

Phonics: /f/f
Say the name of each picture. Write the letter next to each picture
whose name begins with the /f/ sound.

fit pot Tom

🍎

fit
→

_____
- - - - fit - - - -
_____

★

pot
→

_____
- - - - - - - - - - - - - - - - - - - -
_____

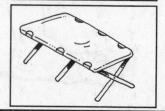

🌲

Tom
→

_____
- - - - - - - - - - - - - - - - - - - -
_____

Phonics: Blending f, o
Blend the sounds and say the word. Write the word. Then circle the
picture that goes with the word.

©Macmillan/McGraw-Hill

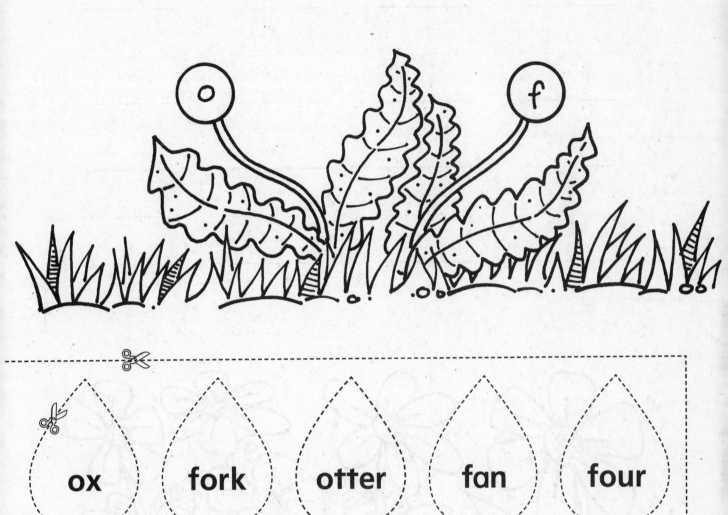

ox	fork	otter	fan	four
octopus	fish	olive	farm	on

Phonics: /o/o, /f/f
Cut out the petals. Look at each word and name its beginning letter and sound. Glue each word on the flower with the same letter as its beginning sound.

Name _____

o

f

Phonics: /o/o /f/f
Practice saying and writing the letters o and f.

Hh

Name _____

I.

h

2.

3.

Phonics: /h/*h*
Say the name of each picture. Write the letter below each picture
whose name begins with the /h/ sound.

Name _____

1.

2.

Comprehension: Main Idea and Details
Look at each picture. Tell what you see. What are these pictures
mainly about? 1. Circle the picture that shows a boy helping.
2. Circle the picture that shows a girl with her pet.

We Are

We are at the ___ store.

©Macmillan/McGraw-Hill

(1)

We are ___ home!

High-Frequency Word: *are*
Read the book aloud to a partner.
Reread for fluency.

(4) Unit 6: Neighborhood • Week 1

We are at the  bakery .

We are at the  park .

Phonemic Awareness: /h/
Look at the picture. Say the name of each item. Circle the item
if its name begins with the same sound you hear at the
beginning of *horse*.

1.

hat 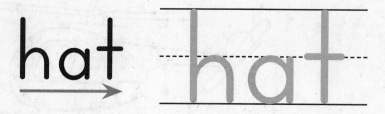 hat

2.

ham _____

3.

hot _____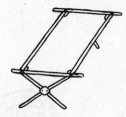

4.

hop _____

Phonics: Blending _h_
Blend the sounds and say the word. Write the word. Circle the
picture that goes with the word.

Dd

Name _____

1.

d

2.

3.

4.

©Macmillan/McGraw-Hill

Phonics: /d/d

Say the name of each picture. Circle the picture whose name begins
with the same sound as *duck*. Write the letter.

Name _____

I.

2.

©Macmillan/McGraw-Hill

Comprehension: Main Idea and Details
Look at each picture. Tell what you see. What are both pictures
mainly about? Color the picture that shows an owl going to the
eye doctor.

For You

I have a cap.

It is for you.

Name _____

High-Frequency Words: *for, you*
Read the book aloud to a
partner. Reread for fluency.

It is for you.

I have a

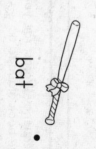
bat

Rr

Name _____

1.

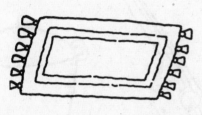

r

2.

3.

4.

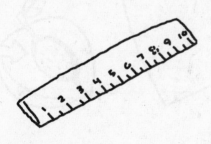

Phonics: /r/r
Say the name of each picture. Circle the picture whose name begins
with the same sound as *rainbow*. Write the letter.

I.

rod   r͞o͞d

2.

red _____

3.

rip _____

Phonics: Blending r
Blend the sounds and say the word. Write the word. Circle the
picture that goes with the word.

Hh

Name _____

Write

1.

h   ‑ ‑ ‑ ‑ ‑ ‑ ‑ ‑ ‑ ‑ ‑   ‑ ‑ ‑ ‑ ‑ ‑ ‑ ‑ ‑ ‑ ‑

2.

‑ ‑ ‑ ‑ ‑ ‑ ‑ ‑ ‑ ‑ ‑   ‑ ‑ ‑ ‑ ‑ ‑ ‑ ‑ ‑ ‑ ‑   ‑ ‑ ‑ ‑ ‑ ‑ ‑ ‑ ‑ ‑ ‑

3.

‑ ‑ ‑ ‑ ‑ ‑ ‑ ‑ ‑ ‑ ‑   ‑ ‑ ‑ ‑ ‑ ‑ ‑ ‑ ‑ ‑ ‑   ‑ ‑ ‑ ‑ ‑ ‑ ‑ ‑ ‑ ‑ ‑

Phonics: /h/*h*
Say the name of each picture. Write the letter below each picture
whose name begins with the /h/ sound.

Name _____

Comprehension: Retell

Look at the pictures and listen to the story. *The girl draws a picture. It is for her dad. The girl gives the picture to her dad.* Circle the picture that shows the end of the story. Retell the story to a partner.

Are You Sad?

Are you sad?

©Macmillan/McGraw-Hill

Name _____

I like you!

High-Frequency Words: *are, for, you*
Read the book aloud to a partner.
Reread for fluency.

I am sad.

I have a  flower for you.

3

Write

1.

d

2.

3.

Phonics: /d/d, /r/r
Say the name of each picture. Then write the letter that stands
for the sound you hear at the beginning of the word. Repeat the
names aloud.

am nap can

1. _____

I am a cat.

2.   _____

I like to _____ .

3. _____

I _____ nap.

Phonics: Blending *am, ap, an*
Read the sentence. Write the word that completes the sentence.
Read the sentence again.

Name _____

I.

2.

Comprehension: Main Idea/Details *A Rainy Day*
Look at each picture. Tell what you see. What are the pictures
mainly about? Circle the pictures that show rainy weather.

Ee

Name _____

1.

 _____

e

 _____

2.

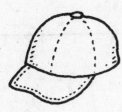 _____

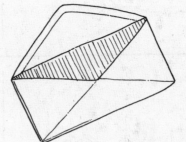 _____

3.

 _____

Phonics: /e/e
Say the name of each picture. Write the letter next to each
picture whose name begins with the /e/ sound.

I can do this!

High-Frequency Words: *this, do*
Read the book aloud to a partner.
Reread for fluency.

④ Unit 7: Weather • Week 1

Can You?

Can you do this?

①

I can do this!

Can you do this?

I.

 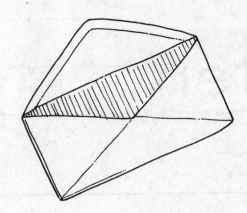

2.

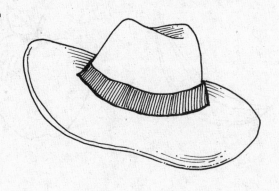 

3.

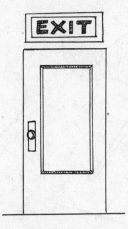 

Phonemic Awareness: /e/

Say the name of each item. Circle the item if its name begins
with the same sound you hear at the beginning of *egg*.

Write

Name _____

1.

ten

ten

10   5

2.

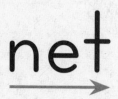
red

3.

net

Phonics: Blending e
Blend the sounds and say the word. Write the word.
Then circle the picture that goes with the word.

©Macmillan/McGraw-Hill

 146   Unit 7: Weather • Week 1

Bb

Name _____

I.

   b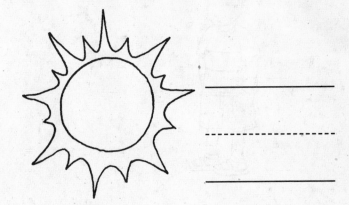

2.

   _____   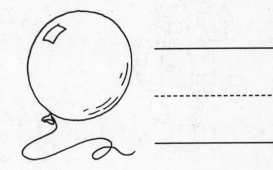   _____

3.

   _____      _____

Phonics: /b/ b
Say the name of each picture. Write the letter next to each
picture whose name begins with the /b/ sound.

Name _____

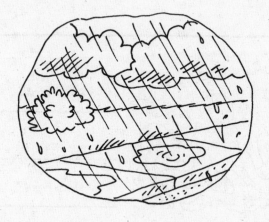

Comprehension: Setting
Draw a line from each child to the correct setting.

What Can You Do?

What can you do?

①

Name _____

I can sit and nap.

High-Frequency Words: *and, what*
Read the book aloud to a partner.
Reread for fluency.

④ Unit 7: Weather • Week 2

I can hop and hop.

What can you do?

Name _____

1.

_ _ _ _ _ _ _

_ _ _ _ _ _ _

2.

_ _ _ _ _ _ _

_ _ _ _ _ _ _

3.

_ _ _ _ _ _ _

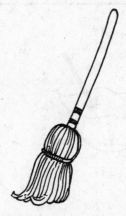

_ _ _ _ _ _ _

Phonics: /l/
Say the name of each picture. Write the letter next to each
picture whose name begins with the /l/ sound.

bed bib lip

1.

(bed)
bit

b̶e̶d̶

2.

pen
bib

3.

lip
lap

Phonics: Blending *b, l*
Blend the sounds and say each word. Look at the picture.
Circle the word that goes with the picture. Write the word.

Ee

Name _____

1.

 e

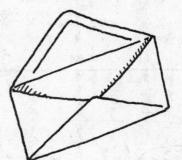

2.

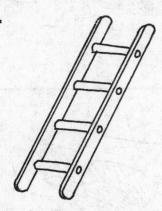

3.

Phonics: /e/e
Say the name of each picture. Write the letter next to each picture whose name begins with the /e/ sound.

Name _____

1.

 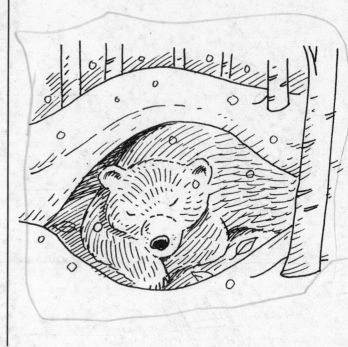

2.

Comprehension: Fantasy/Reality
Look at each picture. Circle the picture that shows something
that might really happen. Draw a line under the picture that
shows something that could not happen.

We Can Do This

©Macmillan/McGraw-Hill

What can you and I do?

Name _____

We can do this.

High-Frequency Words: *this, do, and, what*
Read the book aloud to a partner. Reread
for fluency.

4 Unit 7: Weather • Week 3

We can do this.

What can you and I do?

Bb Ll

Name _____

1.

2.

3.

Phonics: /b/b, /l/l
Say the name of each picture. Write the letter *b* below the picture
if its name begins with the same sound as *bear*. Write the letter *l* if
its name begins with the same sound as *leaf*.

sip pit lid

1.

_____

sip

2.

_____

3.

_____

Phonics: Blending _ip_, _it_, _id_
Blend the sounds and say each word. Look at the picture.
Write the word that goes with the picture.

Name _____

Name _____

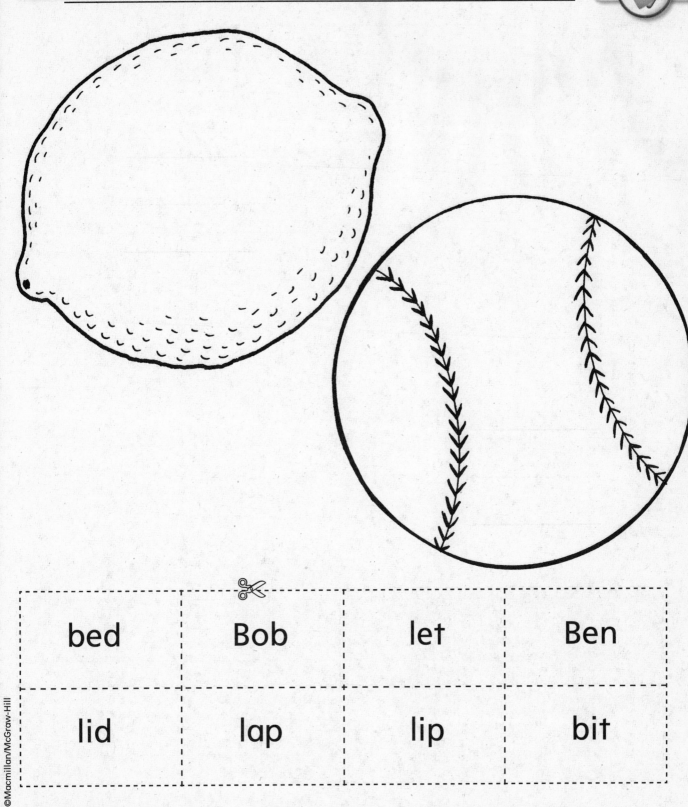

bed	Bob	let	Ben
lid	lap	lip	bit

Phonics: /e/e, /b/b, /l/l
Cut out each word. Blend the sounds and say each word. Glue each
word that begins with the /b/ sound on the *baseball*. Glue each word
that begins with the /l/ sound on the lemon.

Name _____

Phonics: /e/e, /b/b, /l/l

Say the name of each item. Write the letter that stands for the /b/ sound you hear at the beginning of the word *baseball*. Write the letter that stands for the /l/ sound you hear at the beginning of the word *lemon*.

Kk

Write

1.

k

2.

3.

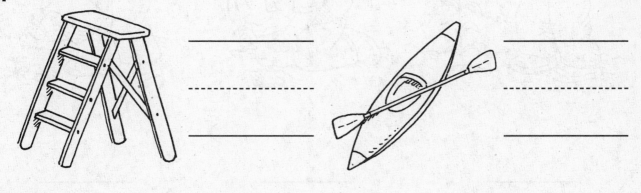

Phonics: /k/ k
Say the name of each picture. Write the letter next to each
picture whose name begins with the /k/ sound.

1.

_____   _____   _____

2.

_____   _____   _____

Comprehension: Sequence
Look at the pictures in each row. Write 1, 2, and 3 to show what
happened first, next, and last.

It Is Little

This is a _____
flower

©Macmillan/McGraw-Hill

Name _____

"It is little," said Pat.

High-Frequency Words: *little, said*
Read the book aloud to a partner.
Reread for fluency.

④ Unit 8: Plants • Week 1

①

"It is little," said Ken.

This is a bug.

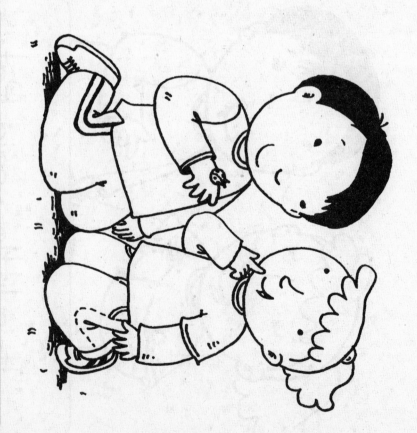

1.

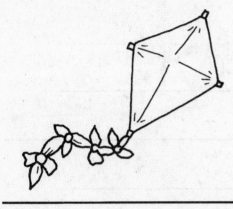  

2.

3.

Phonemic Awareness: /k/
Say the name of each picture. Circle the picture if its name
begins with the same sound you hear at the beginning of *kite*.

I.

ck

2.

3.

4.

Phonics: /k/ck
Say the name of each picture. Write the letters that stand for the
/k/ sound you hear at the end of the word. Repeat the names aloud.

©Macmillan/McGraw-Hill

U u

1.  u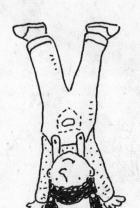

2.

3.

Phonics: /u/u
Say the name of each picture. Write the letter next to each picture
whose name begins with the /u/ sound.

Name _____

1.

2.

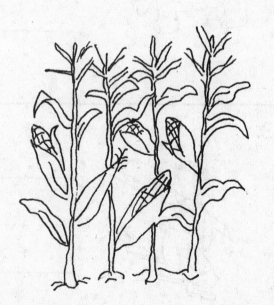

Comprehension: Retell _Seed Secrets_
Use the pictures to retell what happened in the story to a partner.
Color the pictures.

We Are Here!

Tim   Kim   Dan

Tim was here.

①

We are here!

High-Frequency Words: *here, was*
Read the book aloud to a partner.
Reread for fluency.

④ Unit 8: Plants • Week 2

Kim was here.

Dan was here.

Phonemic Awareness: /u/
Look at the pictures. Say the name of each item. Circle the
item if its name begins with the same sound you hear at the
beginning of *umbrella*.

Unit 8: Plants • Week 2   **171**

Name _____

sun cup pup

1.

sun

sun — — — — — —

2.

cup

— — — — — — — — — —

3.

pup

— — — — — — — — — —

Phonics: Blending *u*
Blend the sounds and say the word. Write the word. Then
circle the picture that goes with the word.

©Macmillan/McGraw-Hill

Name _____

I.

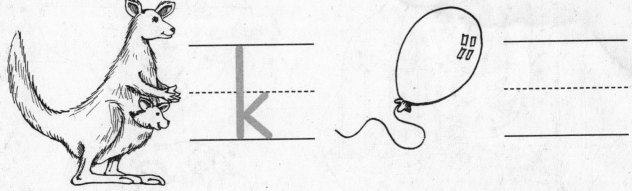

k _ _ _ _ _ _

2.

3.

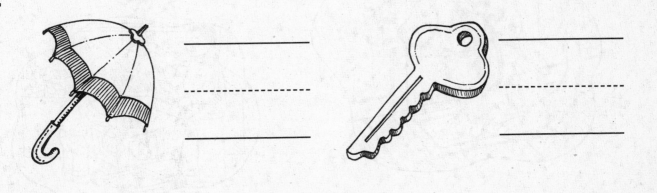

Phonics: /k/ k
Say the name of each picture. Write the letter next to each
picture whose name begins with the /k/ sound.

©Macmillan/McGraw-Hill

Unit 8: Plants • Week 3   **173**

1.

2.

Comprehension: Draw Conclusions
Look at the picture on the left. Draw a line to the picture on the
right that shows what may happen.

This Is Little

Name _____

"Bud was a little cub.

High-Frequency Words: *little, said, here, was*
Read the book aloud to a partner.
Reread for fluency.

④ Unit 8: Plants • Week 3

"This is little," said Nat.

①

"This is little," said Dot.

"Here is Bud!" said Dot.

Uu

Name _____

1.

_____   _____   _____

u

-------------------------   -------------------------   -------------------------

_____   _____   _____

2.

_____   _____   _____

-------------------------   -------------------------   -------------------------

_____   _____   _____

3.

_____   _____   _____

-------------------------   -------------------------   -------------------------

_____   _____   _____

©Macmillan/McGraw-Hill

Phonics: /u/u

Say the name of each picture. Write the letter below each
picture whose name begins with the /u/ sound.

sick kick pick

1.

sick   sick

2.

kick

3.

pick

Phonics: Blending *ick*
Blend the sounds and say the word. Write the word.

i

u

sun

kick

fun

kit

pup

sick

Phonics: /i/i, /u/u, /k/k, /k/ck

Cut out the leaves. Read the words. If a leaf has a word with the /i/
sound, glue it next to the letter *i*. If a leaf has a word with the /u/
sound, glue it next to the letter *u*.

Phonics: /i/i, /u/u, /k/k, /k/ck

Cut out the leaves. Read the words. If a leaf has a word with the /i/
sound, glue it next to the letter *i*. If a leaf has a word with the /u/
sound, glue it next to the letter *u*.

Gg

Name _____

I.

_____

‑ ‑ ‑ ‑ g ‑ ‑ ‑ ‑

_____

_____

‑ ‑ ‑ ‑ ‑ ‑ ‑ ‑

_____

2.

_____

‑ ‑ ‑ ‑ ‑ ‑ ‑ ‑

_____

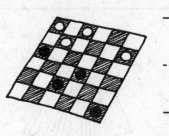

_____

‑ ‑ ‑ ‑ ‑ ‑ ‑ ‑

_____

3.

_____

‑ ‑ ‑ ‑ ‑ ‑ ‑ ‑

_____

_____

‑ ‑ ‑ ‑ ‑ ‑ ‑ ‑

_____

4.

_____

‑ ‑ ‑ ‑ ‑ ‑ ‑ ‑

_____

_____

‑ ‑ ‑ ‑ ‑ ‑ ‑ ‑

_____

Phonics: /g/g
Say the name of each picture. Write the letter next to each picture
whose name begins with the /g/ sound.

1.

2.

 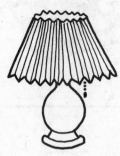  

3.

   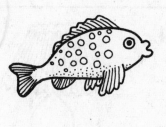

Comprehension: Classify and Categorize
Look at each picture. Draw an X on the picture that
does not belong. Tell why it does not belong.

©Macmillan/McGraw-Hill

Kim and Dan

She is Kim.

Name _____

He can hop.

High-Frequency Words: _she, he_
Read the book aloud to a partner.
Reread for fluency.

④ Unit 9: Amazing Creatures • Week I

①

She can run.

He is Dan.

Ww

Name _____

Write

1.

 _____ W  _____

2.

 _____  _____

3.

 _____  _____

4.

 _____  _____

Phonics: /w/w
Say the name of each picture. Write the letter next to each
picture whose name begins with the /w/ sound.

Name _____

web wet wig

1.

web    web

2.

wet

3.

wig

Phonics: Blending w
Blend the sounds and say the word. Write the word. Circle the
picture that goes with the word.

I.

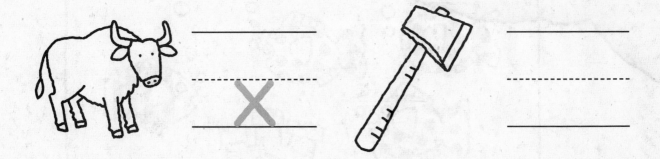

_____

- - - - - x - - - - -

_____

_____

- - - - - - - - - -

_____

2.

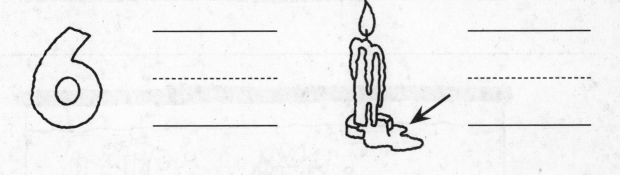

_____

- - - - - - - - - -

_____

_____

- - - - - - - - - -

_____

3.

_____

- - - - - - - - - -

_____

_____

- - - - - - - - - -

_____

Phonics: /ks/x

Say the name of each picture. Write the letter that stands for the /ks/ sound you hear at the end of each word.

I.

2.

Comprehension: Compare and Contrast *Fish Faces*
Look at each picture. Circle all the fish that are the same.
Draw an X on the fish that is different. Tell how the fish
are the same and different.

Look At This

Look at this .

ladybug

©Macmillan/McGraw-Hill

Name _____

It has))) .

stripes

High-Frequency Words: *has, look*
Read the book aloud to a partner.
Reread for fluency.

4 Unit 9: Amazing Creatures • Week 2

It has  spots.

Look at this  bee.

bee

Name _____

I.

_____

- - - - - - - - - - - - - -

_____

V

2.

_____

- - - - - - - - - - - - - -

_____

3.

_____

- - - - - - - - - - - - - -

_____

4.

_____

- - - - - - - - - - - - - -

_____

©Macmillan/McGraw-Hill

Phonics: /v/v

Say the name of each picture. Write the letter next to
each picture whose name begins with the /v/ sound.

1.

pig

(six)

six

2.

box

bag

3.

vet

web

4.

pan

van

Phonics: Blending x, v
Look at the picture. Blend the sounds and say each word. Circle
the word that goes with the picture. Then write the word.

©Macmillan/McGraw-Hill

Name _____

I.

 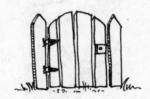 (girl)

_____

- - - - - - - - - - -

g

2.

_____

- - - - - - - - - - -

_____

3.

_____

- - - - - - - - - - -

_____

4.

_____

- - - - - - - - - - -

_____

Phonics: /g/g, /w/w
I. 2. Say the name of each picture. Circle each picture whose name begins with the same sound as *gate*. Write the letter.
3. 4. Say the name of each picture. Circle each picture whose name begins with the same sound as *wagon*. Write the letter.

Unit 9: Amazing Creatures • Week 3   **193**

Name _____

1.

2.

Comprehension: Fantasy and Reality
Look at each picture. Circle the one that shows something that might really happen. Draw a line under the one that shows something that could not happen.

Ben and Kat

Look at Ben.

Name _____

She has a fan.

High-Frequency Words: *she, he, look, has*
Read the book aloud with a partner.
Reread for fluency.

(4) Unit 9: Amazing Creatures • Week 3

(1)

He has a top.

Look at Kat!

1.

2.

3.

4.

Phonics: /ks/x, /v/v

1. 2. Say the name of each picture. Circle each picture whose name ends with the same sound as *fox*. Write the letter.

3. 4. Say the name of each picture. Circle each picture whose name begins with the same sound as *van*. Write the letter.

I.

Ned
Deb

Ned

2.

red
bed

_____

3.

pen
pot

_____

4. 10

ten
top

_____

©Macmillan/McGraw-Hill

Phonics: Blending _ed_, _en_
Look at each picture. Blend the sounds to read each word. Circle the
word that goes with the picture. Then write the word.

Phonemic Awareness: /g/, /w/
Say the name of each picture. Put a marker on each picture whose
name begins with the same sound as *gate*. Play again. Put a marker
on each picture whose name begins with the same sound as *wagon*.

Name _____

Phonemic Awareness: /ks/, /v/

Say the name of each picture. Put a marker on each picture whose name ends with the same sound as *fox*. Play again. Put a marker on each picture whose name begins with the same sound as *van*.

Jj

Name _____

 Write

1.

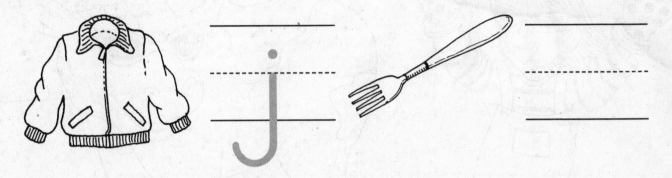

_____

j _____

_____ _____

2.

_____ _____

_____ _____

_____ _____

3.

_____ _____

_____ _____

_____ _____

©Macmillan/McGraw-Hill

Phonics: /j/j
Say the name of each picture. Write the letter next to
each picture whose name begins with the /j/ sound.

Name _____

Comprehension: Use Illustrations *What Do You Know!*
Look at the picture. Circle the things that come in twos.

My Dog Mack

This is my dog Mack.

Name _____

I nap with Mack.

High-Frequency Words: *with, my*
Read the book aloud to a partner.
Reread for fluency.

4   Unit 10: I Know A Lot! • Week 1

I play with Mack.

Look at my dog go!

Q q

Name _____

1.

_____

qu

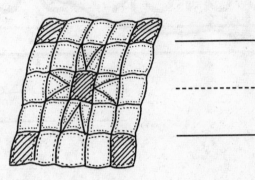

_____

- - - - - - - - - - -

_____

2.

_____

- - - - - - - - - - -

_____

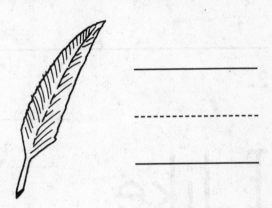

_____

- - - - - - - - - - -

_____

3.

_____

- - - - - - - - - - -

_____

_____

- - - - - - - - - - -

_____

Phonics: /kw/ *qu*
Say the name of each picture. Write the letters that stand for
the /kw/ sound you hear at the beginning of each word. Repeat
the names aloud.

quick Jack quack

1.

I am quick.

2.

I like _____.

3.

Jack can _____.

Phonics: Blending *j*, *qu*
Blend the sounds and say the word. Read the sentence.
Write the word that completes the sentence. Read the
sentence again.

1.

2.

3.

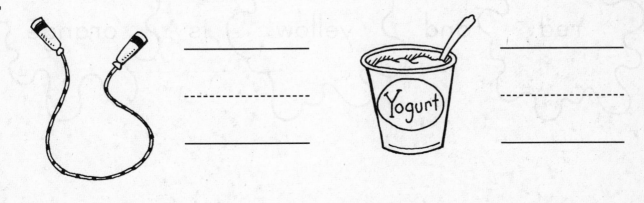

Phonics: /y/y

Say the name of each picture. Write the letter next to
each picture whose name begins with the /y/ sound.

Name _____

I.

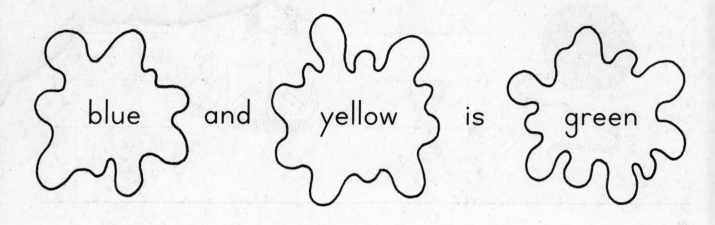

blue and yellow is green

2.

red and yellow is orange

Comprehension: Cause and Effect *Warthogs Paint*
I. Color the first splash blue, the second yellow.
2. Color the first splash red, the second yellow. Mix the 2 colors
in the last splash in each row. Name the new colors.

Where is Jon?

Where is Jon?

Name _____

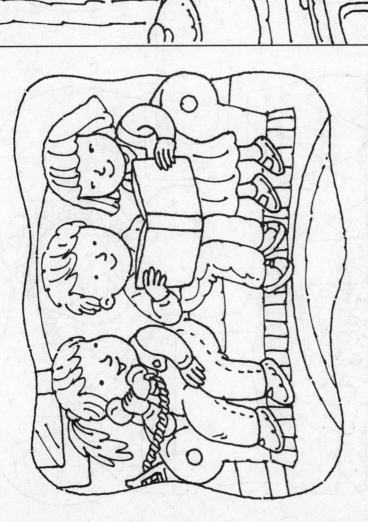

She is here with me.

High-Frequency Words: *me, where*
Read the book aloud to a partner.
Reread for fluency.

④ Unit 10: I Know A Lot! • Week 2

①

He is here with me.

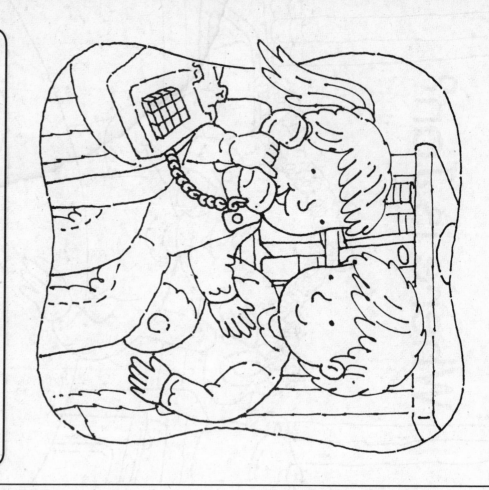

Where is Kat?

Zz

Name _____

1.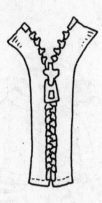

z

2. O

3.

Phonics: /z/z
Say the name of each picture. Write the letter next to
each picture whose name begins with the /z/ sound.

Zeb zip →

1.

I am Zeb .

2.

I can _____
_____ .

3.

I like to _____
_____ .

©Macmillan/McGraw-Hill

Phonics: Blending z
Blend the sounds and say the word. Read each sentence.
Write the word that completes the sentence. Read it again.

I.

_____   _____   _____

qu   j

2.

_____   _____   _____

_____   _____   _____

_____   _____   _____

3.

_____   _____   _____

_____   _____   _____

_____   _____   _____

Phonics: /j/j, /kw/qu
Say the name of each picture. Then write the letter that stands
for the sound you hear at the beginning of the word. Repeat
the names aloud.

Circle

Name _____

I.

2.

©Macmillan/McGraw-Hill

Comprehension: Setting

1. Look at the pictures. Circle the one that shows animals at a pond.
2. Look at the pictures. Circle the one that shows animals in a tree.

Where Is My Bat?

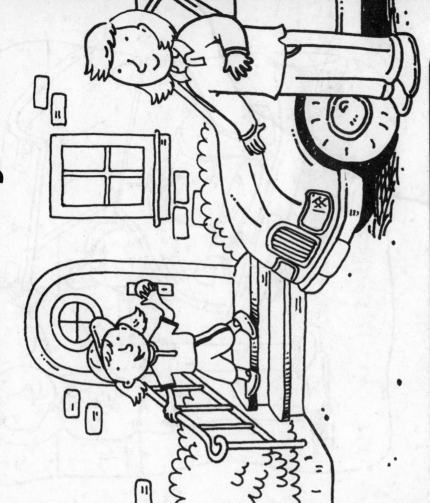

Where is my bat?

(1)

Name _____

It is here with me.

High-Frequency Words: *with, my,*
me, where
Read the book aloud to a partner.
Reread for fluency.

(4) Unit 10: I Know A Lot! • Week 3

It is here with me.

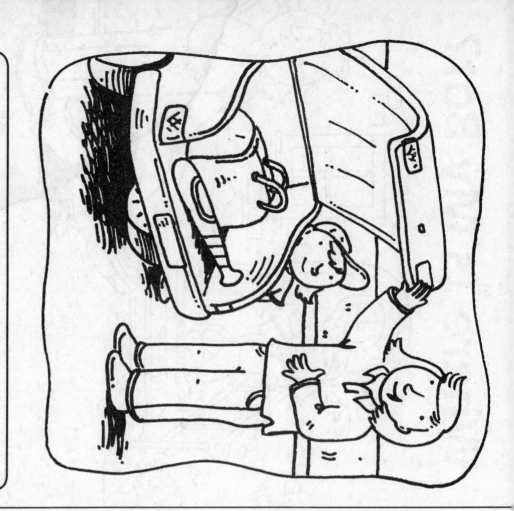

Where is my bag?

Name _____

1.

y

2.

0

3.

Phonics: /y/y, /z/z

Say the name of each picture. Then write the letter that stands
for the sound you hear at the beginning of the word. Repeat the
names aloud.

run pup nut

1.

My pup and I ___ run ___.

2.

My ___ Pup ___ has fun.

3.

He has a ___ nut ___.

Phonics: Blending un, up, ut
Blend the sounds and say the word. Read the sentence. Write the
word that completes the sentence. Read the sentence again.

©Macmillan/McGraw-Hill

jet

cot

sun | fan | pig

sick

Phonics: *Rhyming Words*
Cut on the dotted lines. Fold on the solid lines and tape together.
Take turns tossing the cube with a partner. Read the word that
ends up on top. Then say a word that rhymes with it.

Name _____

Phonics: *Rhyming Words*
Cut on the dotted lines. Fold on the solid lines and tape together.
Use to play a game with a partner.